VAMPIRES VS WEREWOLVES

DoodleWars

BY OAKLEY GRAHAM + ANDREW PINDER

Sandy Creek
NEW YORK

WITH COLOR-IN STICKERS

For centuries, werewolves had been enslaved to watch over their vampire masters' tombs during daylight hours. Forced to make the painful transformation from man to beast every single day, the werewolves longed to break free from vampire tyranny.

Then in AD 1267, a new hope emerged for the werewolves. Descended directly from the original werewolf blood line, an alpha male werewolf called Maenon was able to control the forced transformations inflicted by the vampires. Free to plot against his vampire masters during the day, Maenon freed pack after pack of his species and started the vampires vs werewolves war.

Finish this picture of werewolves guarding
vampire tombs during the day.

Maenon started the vampires vs werewolves war,
but nobody knows what he looks like.
Blessed with superhuman strength and speed,
Maenon's intelligence means that he is more than a
match for the oldest and most powerful vampires.

In the early days of the war, Maenon led the werewolves to many victories over their vampire enemies.

Can you draw him into this battle scene?

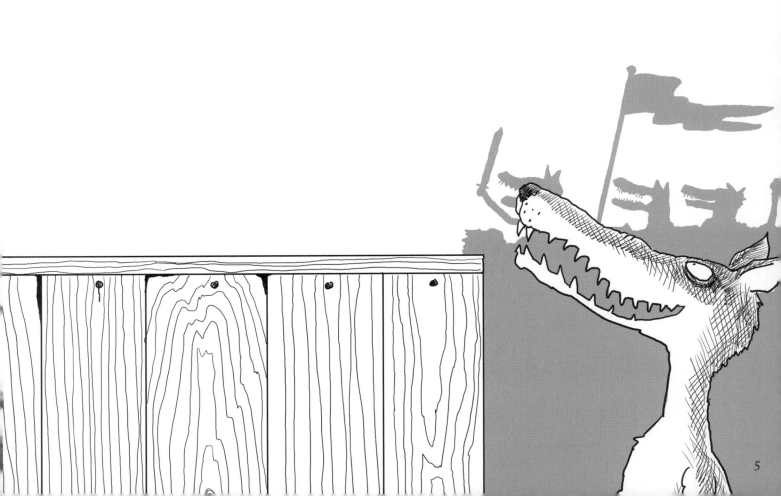

The supreme vampire council is determined to end
the war and to assert their rule over the werewolves.
A meeting of vampire elders is arranged in a catacomb
at a top-secret location.

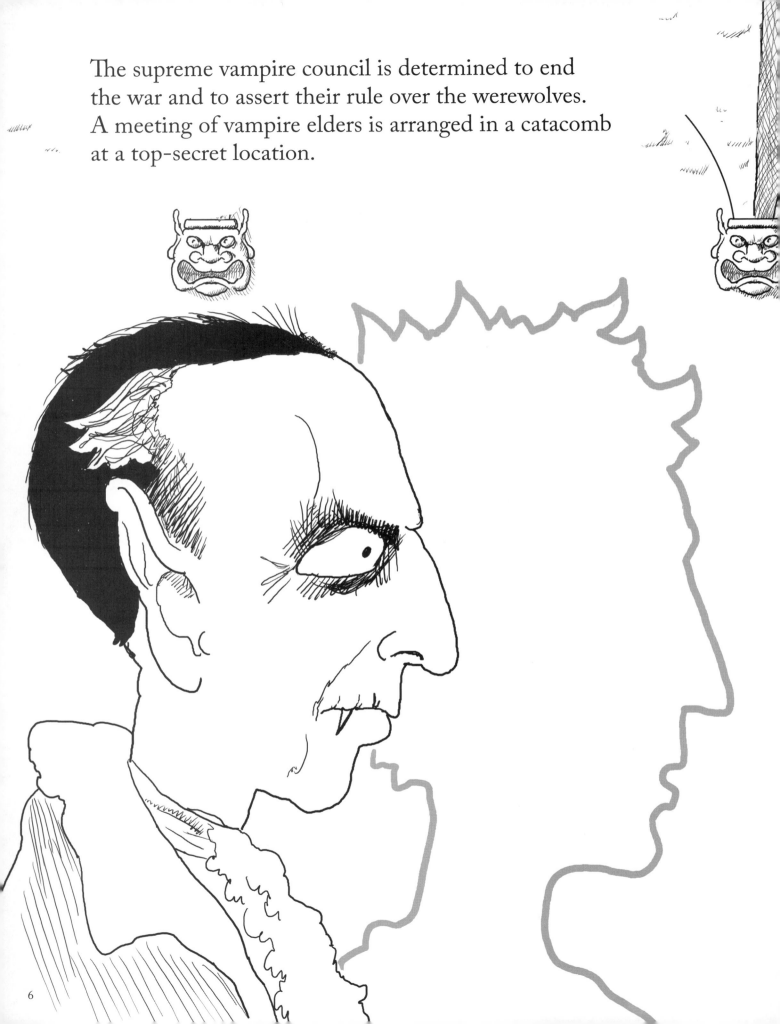

Can you finish the faces of the elite vampire council members?

Before the vampires enslaved the werewolves, their transformation from man to beast only occurred during a full moon.

Add werewolf silhouettes to this forest landscape, bathed in the white light of a full moon.

Maenon is awesome at battle tactics and plans his pack raids against the vampires with military precision. In Maenon's most famous victory, an elite werewolf pack ambushed one of the most ancient vampire clans and inflicted true death on them all (werewolf bites are fatal to vampires).

Can you add the werewolves to this scene as they lie in wait for the vampire clan?

Although Maenon achieved many early victories against the vampires, the werewolf packs suffered many fatalities. The losses increased dramatically when a vampire elder called Marius assembled a squadron of hunters to track down and exterminate marauding werewolf packs.

Marius's squadron of vampire hunters march under a foreboding black flag.

Can you design a battle flag that will strike terror into the hearts of everyone who sees it?

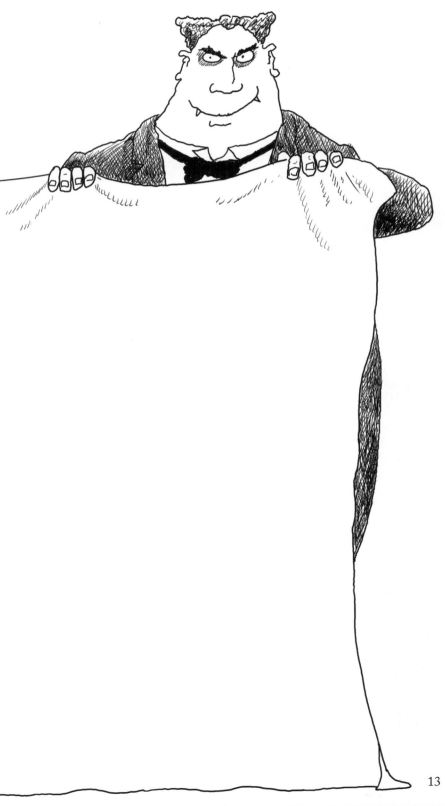

Maenon's werewolves suffered heavy losses at the hands of Marius's squadron. At the battle of the Catskill Mountains, Marius personally slayed an entire pack! Marius possesses superhuman strength and is a master of many different types of weapons.

Can you complete Marius's
impressive weapon armory?

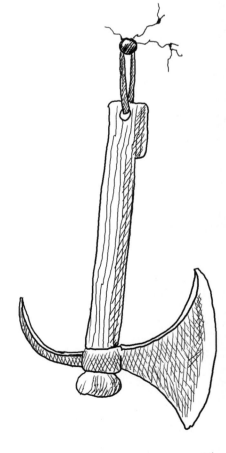

The war between the supernatural enemies raged for years. During this time human kings and queens were forced to pledge their allegiance to either the vampires or the werewolves.

Complete the coat of arms for each king or queen who has pledged allegiance to either the vampires or werewolves.

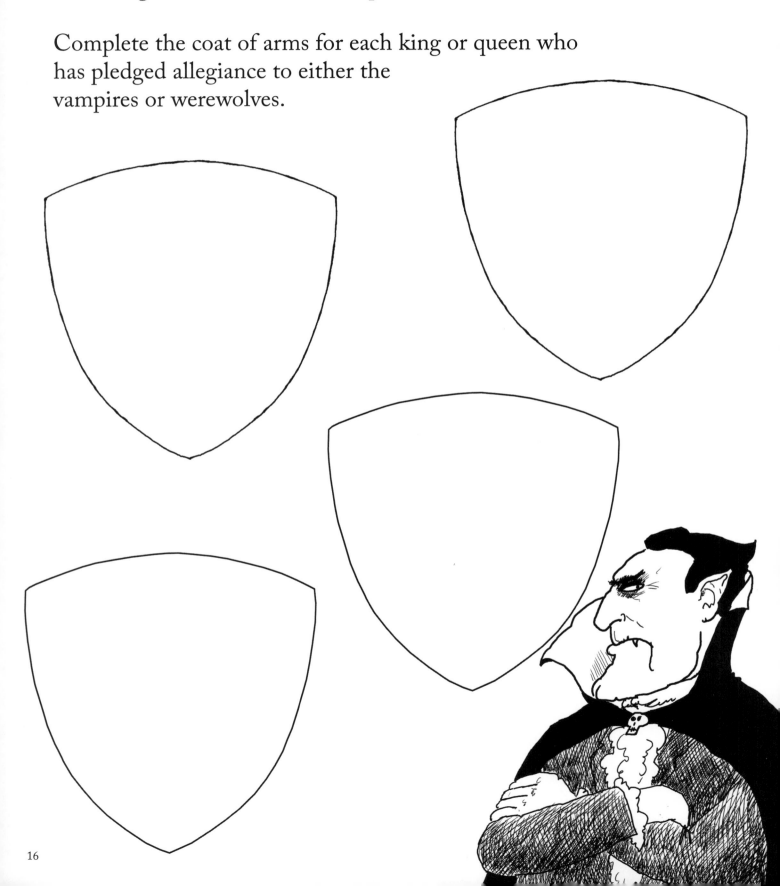

The vampires favored human allies who possessed heavily fortified castles where they could sleep safely during the daylight hours.

Add a castle to this mountainous scene.

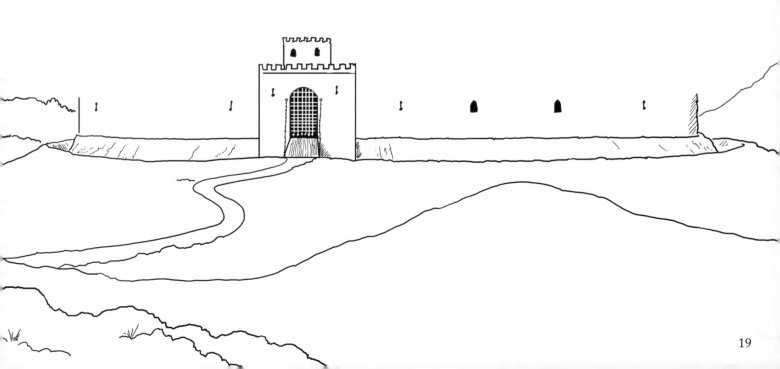

Meanwhile, the werewolves sought allies from human tribes of hunter-gatherers. The forests provided the werewolves with sanctuary and a place to recover after battle.

Complete this woodland clearing scene.
It is the base camp of the mighty Maenon.

Werewolves do not always take on a wolf-like form.
Most of the time, they look just like you and me.
However, under Maenon's tutoring, the werewolves
have developed the ability to change at will.

The transformation from man to beast is very painful and can be terrifying to watch!

Complete the missing transformation stages below.

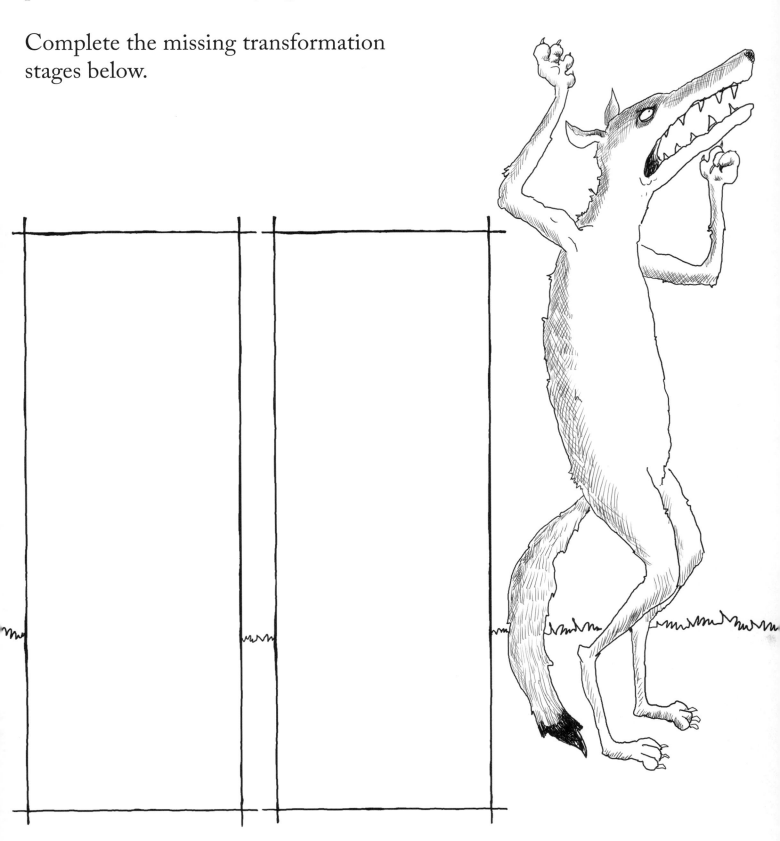

Stalking their werewolf prey under the cover of darkness, nobody has ever lived to provide a description of Marius's bloodthirsty vampire squadron.

Complete the faces of the undead vampire soldiers below.

Marius is a member of the ancient Vlad clan of vampires. His clan is one of five that is directly descended from the original pure bloodline. Together the five ancient clans act as judge and jury on all vampire matters. The clan elders are the leaders of the Supreme Vampire Council.

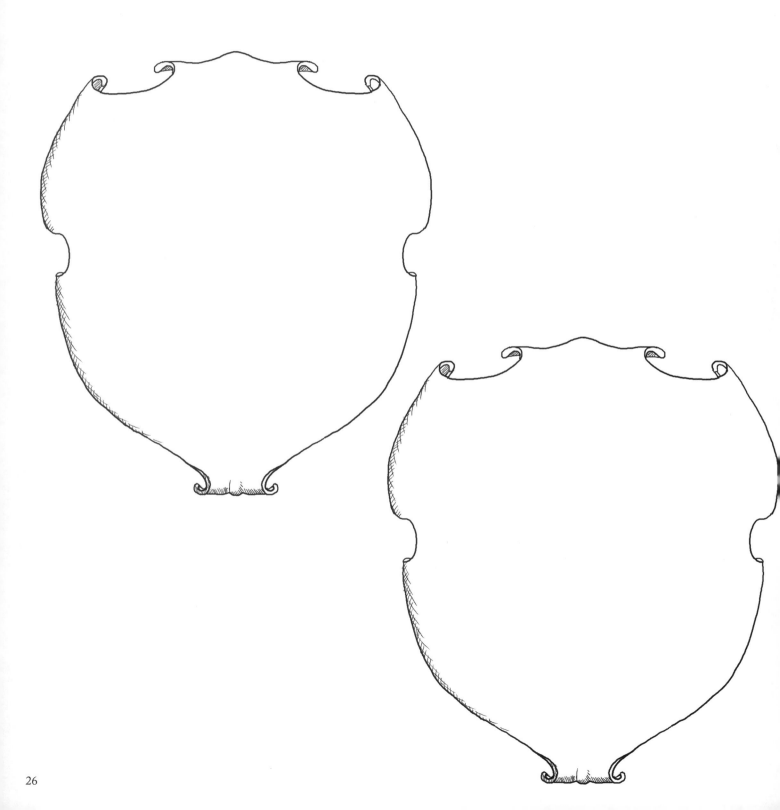

Design an insignia for
each of the five original
bloodline vampire clans.

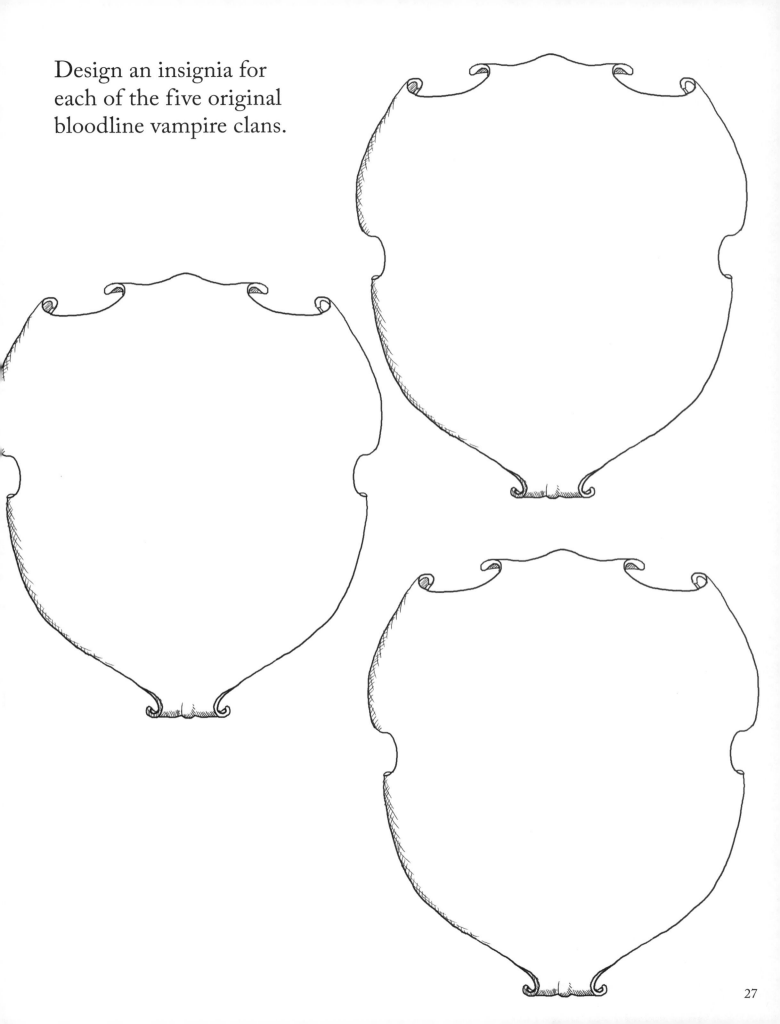

Now create different insignia for the Supreme Vampire Council.
Marius will decide which design is best!

Suffering more and more defeats, the werewolves enlist the help of other supernatural forest dwellers to help them in their war against the vampires. Centaurs, unicorns and fauns all agree to help protect the werewolves in their native forest habitat.

Add the mysterious mythical
creatures to this woodland
glade scene.

31

Sensing that the werewolves are close to defeat, Marius also seeks out allies to help him crush the werewolf rebellion once and for all. Pacts are formed with ogres, dark wizards, bad fairies and many other evil creatures!

The vampire allies meet Marius at his castle to plan their assault on Maenon's base camp in the forest.

Add them to the scene.

Ogres are not the brightest of
supernatural creatures and are easily
manipulated by Marius.

Draw the ogres as they stand guard
outside one of his castles.

A werewolf spy informs Maenon that the vampires are
planning an all-out assault on the forest base camp.
Maenon's pack immediately starts fortifying
the camp with extra defenses
and booby traps.

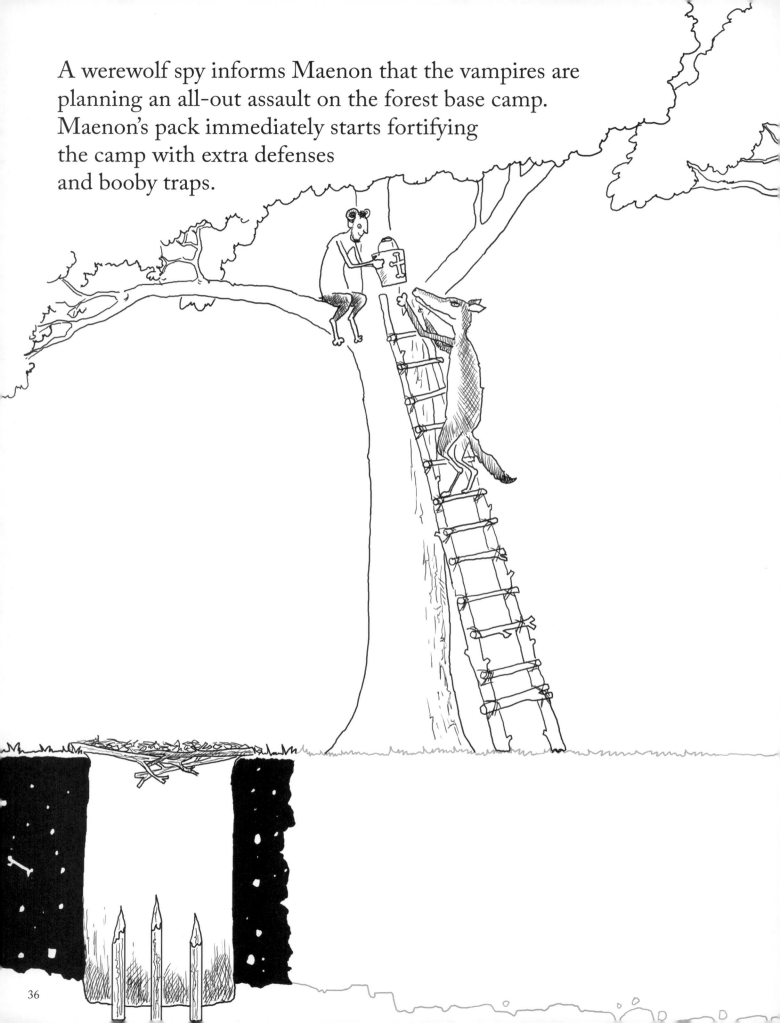

Help Maenon to fortify the forest camp by inventing some booby traps of your own. Remember, vampires don't like silver or holy water and can be staked through the heart to meet their one true death!

Marius assembles vampire squadrons from each of the original bloodline clans for his assault on Maenon's base camp. They are going to sail into the forest on mighty armored ships.

Add the vampire sailing armada to the busy river scene.

Marius's command boat is heavily armed and has a battering ram and foreboding Vlad clan designs on the main sails.

Finish the ship by adding its arsenal of weapons and scary vampiric sail design.

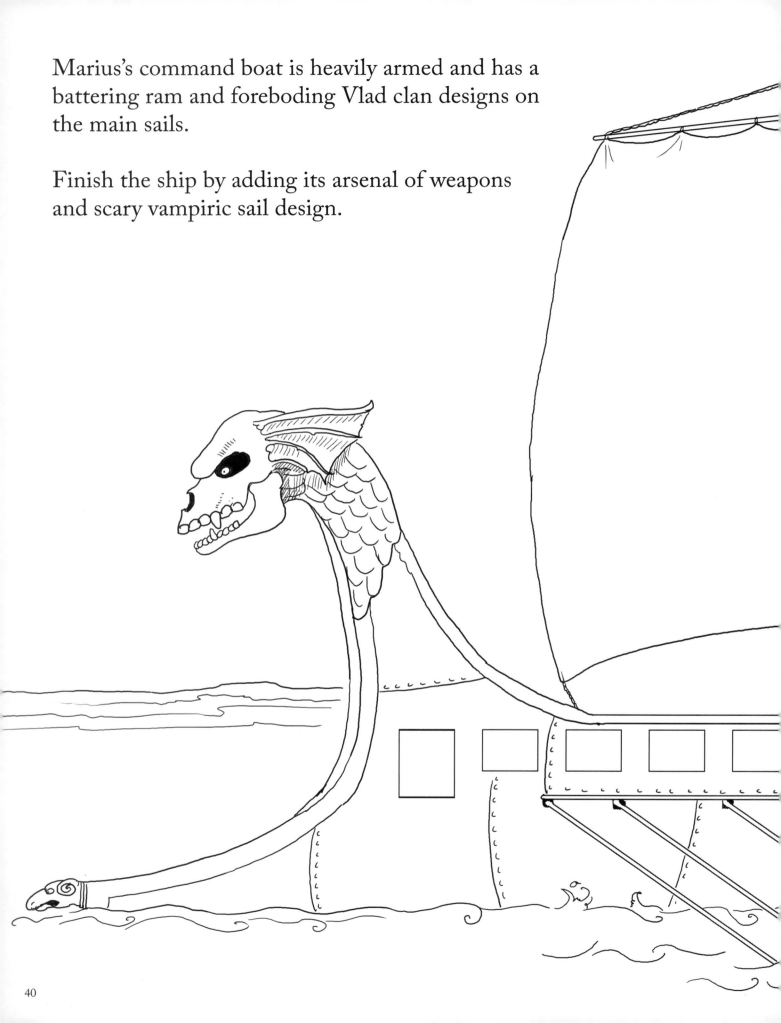

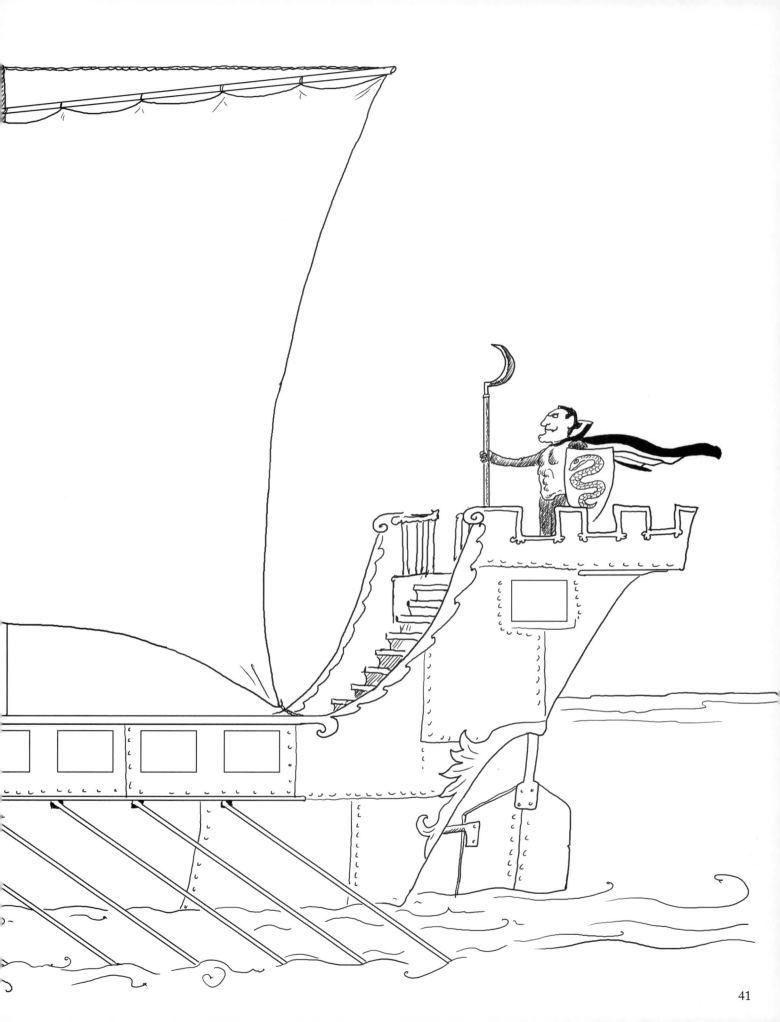

During the voyage down the river, the vampire armada is attacked by a kraken that has strayed inland from the ocean. The kraken looks like a giant octopus and smashes one of the vampire ships to smithereens.

Add the mighty sea beast to the scene.

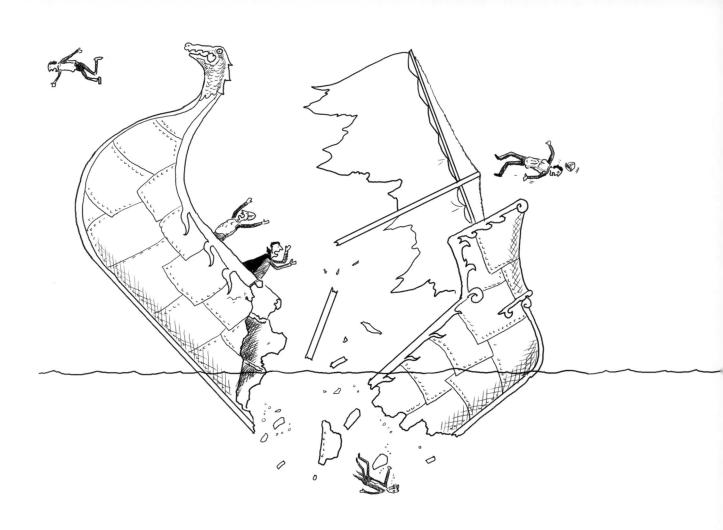

Although the vampires lose a ship to the sea monster attack, they are not deterred and sail into the werewolves' forest under the cover of darkness. The forest echoes with the sound of startled mythical creatures who are watching the vampire soldiers prepare to do battle in their forest realm.

Draw in the mysterious creatures that are watching the vampire soldiers sail into the forest.

The vampire fleet drops anchor at the side of the river close to the werewolf base camp. As the vampire advance party prepares to scout the area, they are immediately attacked by a pack of werewolves. The vampires fight gallantly and manage to kill some of the pack, but they are hopelessly outnumbered and are soon defeated. As the werewolf bites take effect, the vampires are reduced to piles of smoldering ash.

As the rest of the vampire squadrons head into the woods,
they come across the ashes of their fallen comrades.

Add the ash piles to this eerie woodland scene.

Marius is furious that his advance party has been slayed! Unsheathing his sword, he runs into the forest, determined to capture the marauding werewolves. Unable to see through the thick foliage, Marius transforms into a bat and flies above the forest canopy, searching for the werewolves that dared to attack his army.

The werewolves sense danger and flee the scene.

Add the werewolves into the scene as they try
to escape the vampire elder.

Meanwhile, back at the werewolf base camp, Maenon and his pack are enjoying a hearty meal to give them strength for the battle ahead. A long banquet table is laden with delicious werewolf food.

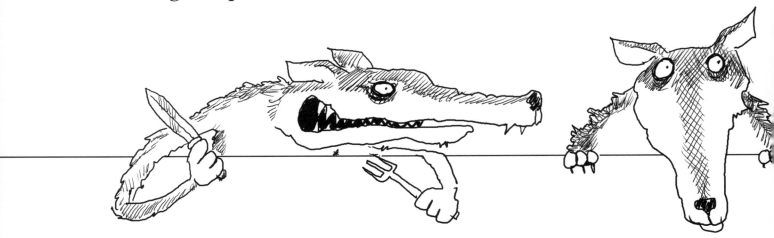

Add the strange food and drink items to this scene.

Marius spies the marauding werewolf pack as they try to escape. He transforms back into his vampire form and chases after them. The young wolf pack is no match for Marius's superhuman strength and combat skills!

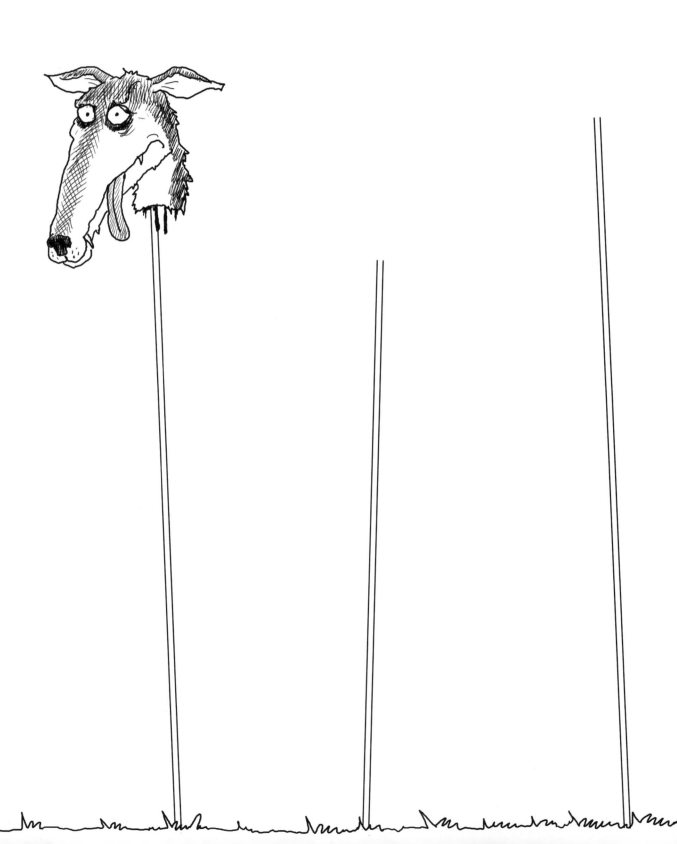

To show his contempt for Maenon, Marius places the heads of the marauders on poles in a forest clearing.

Complete this grisly scene to send a terrifying warning to Maenon!

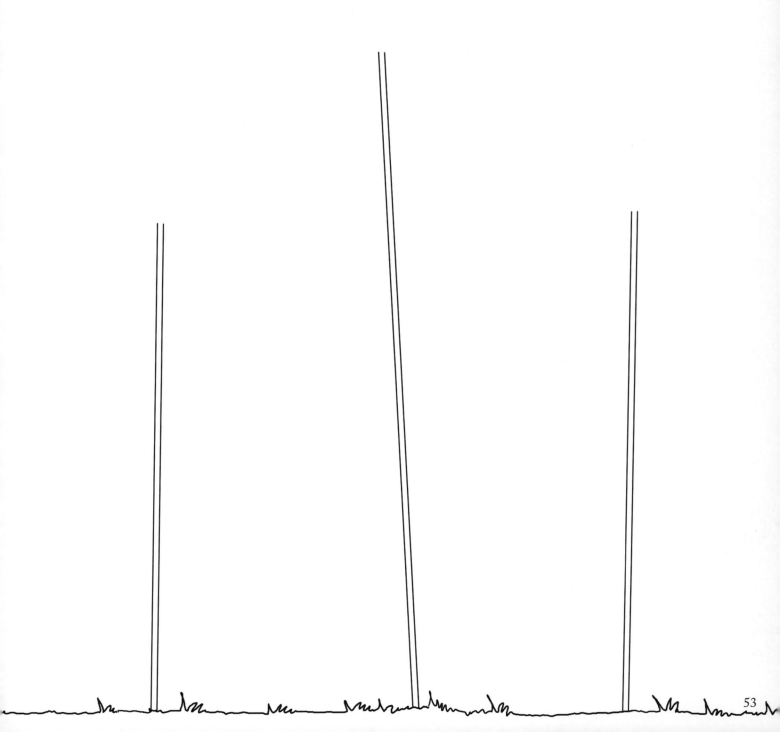

The centaurs are not pleased by Marius's disregard for their forest! The alpha centaur gathers his herd and they gallop to Maenon's base camp to warn him of the vampire advance.

Add the herd as they follow the alpha male.

Centaurs have inhabited ancient forests for thousands of years and know every tree, root and branch like the back of their hands.

Draw a forest scene fit for a centaur.

Meanwhile, a coven of witches are meeting to discuss the war between the vampires and the werewolves. Huddled around steaming cauldrons, they vote to see if they will pledge allegiance to either side.

Complete the scene by adding the witches'
haggard faces and pointy hats!

The witches decide not to get involved in the
supernatural conflict and leave the forest on their
broomsticks.

Add the flying witches to the starry night sky.

As dawn approaches, the vampires set up special tents to protect them from the sun. Dark wizards and bad fairies cast protection spells on the tents and ogres guard the entrance to the vampire camp.

Draw the vampire tents and decorate them with the Supreme Vampire Council insignia.

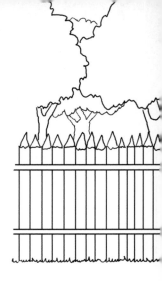

While the vampire army is sleeping, the camp is attacked by the centaurs! However, the centaurs cannot penetrate the dark magic protective ring that surrounds the camp.

Draw a protective ring over the campsite and add the attacking centaurs on the outside.

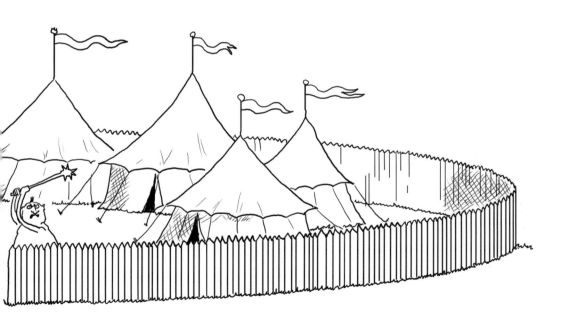

The ogres realize their vampire allies are under attack and challenge the centaurs with their spiked clubs and chains.

Transform these shapes into the ogres' motley selection of weaponry.

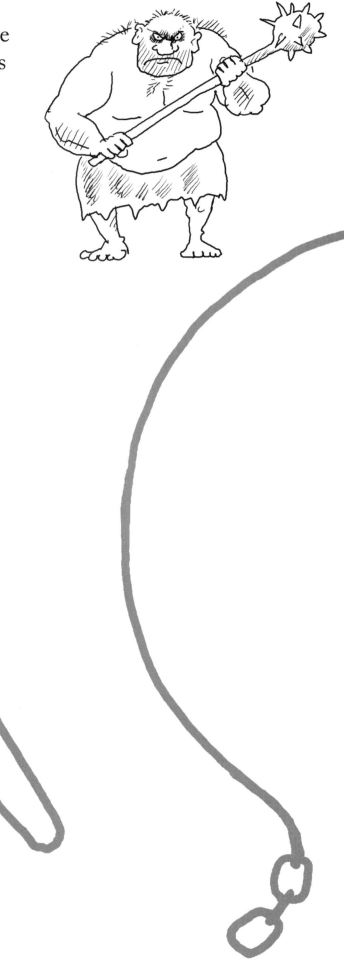

The ogres are just as merciless as their vampire friends and crush the centaurs! As the centaurs try to escape, the bad fairies cast a magic spell to trap them in between the forest and the vampire camp.

Add more centaurs and bad fairies to the scene
as they prepare to cast their wicked spells!

The ogres quickly round up the centaurs and lock them in cages.
Add the unhappy centaurs to the cages.

Don't forget to add the mean-looking ogres standing guard.

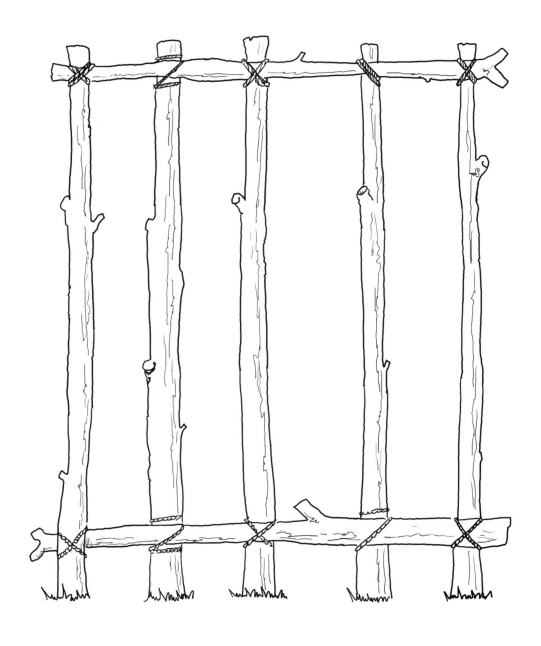

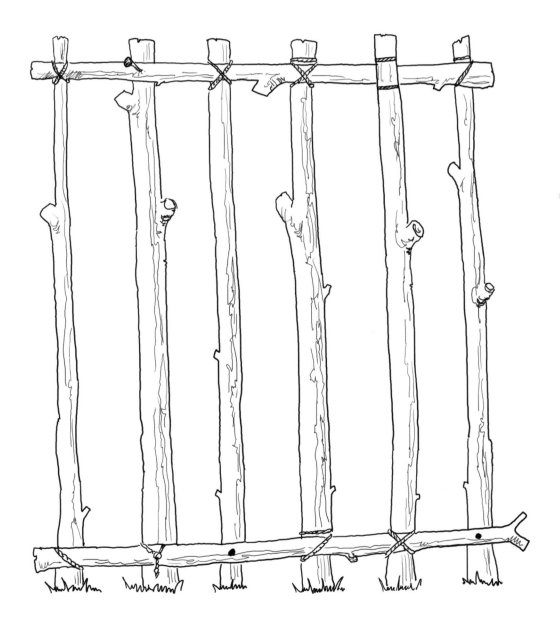

Marius and his vampire squadrons are at the edge of Maenon's base camp and are ready to attack. Suddenly, a herd of unicorns appear! Channeling the energy of the sun through their horns, the unicorns unleash bolts of sunlight into the vampire ranks.

Add more unicorns and bolts of sunlight being fired at the vampires.

Despite the bold attack, the vampire hordes soon overwhelm the unicorns and rush to attack Maenon's base camp.

Add the vampires to the scene as
they charge into the base camp.

The vampires and werewolves fight tooth and claw and it is hard to tell which side is winning.

Add vampires and werewolves to make a busy battle scene!

Amidst the chaos of the battle scene, it is clear that Maenon and Marius are by far the most powerful supernatural creatures on the battlefield.

Add armor and weaponry to each of the supernatural leaders.

Marius and Maenon meet on the field of combat and are immediately encircled by their werewolf and vampire kin.

Complete the circle of vampires and werewolves that surrounds the two leaders.

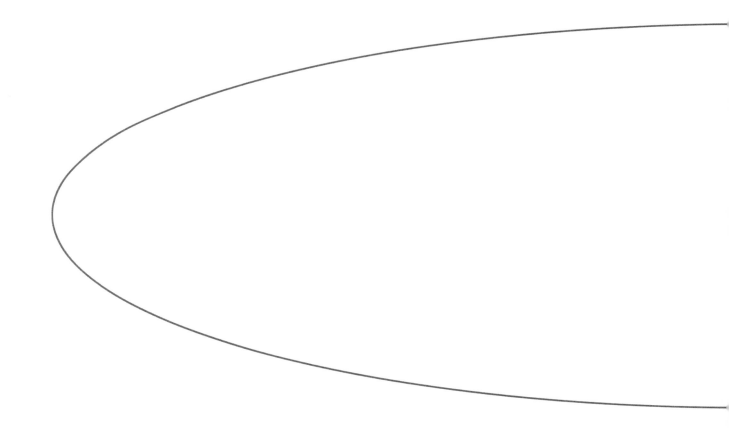

Marius and Maenon agree to fight to the death in order to settle the war once and for all! If Marius wins, the werewolf packs will return to their former masters and will protect the vampires during the day. If Maenon wins, all werewolves will be freed from slavery to the vampires. Both leaders sign a treaty before the fight. The treaty is signed in blood!

Finish writing it for them.

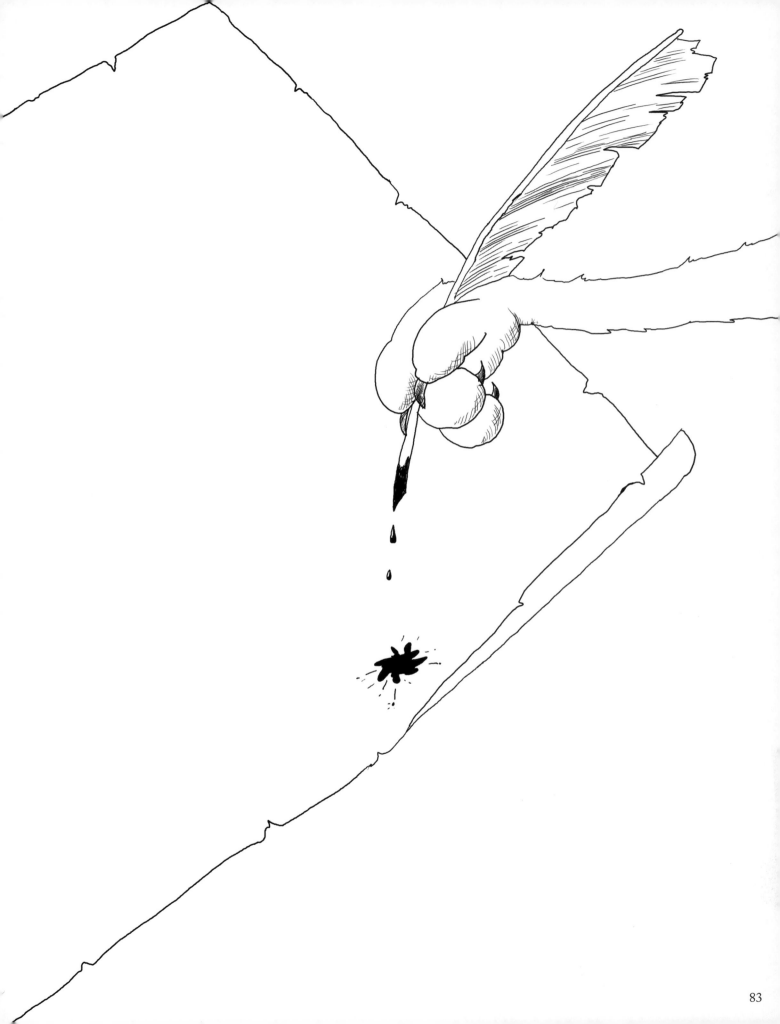

Marius and Maenon circle each other before launching ferocious attacks! Marius is faster and stronger, but Maenon is smarter and can inflict a fatal werewolf bite.

Who wins the battle between the world's most powerful supernatural beings? Draw the winner on the podium.

Following _____'s defeat, the _____ s
have a celebration feast.

Draw the supernatural beings from
the winning side into the scene.

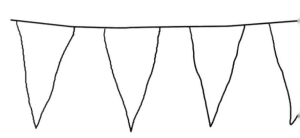

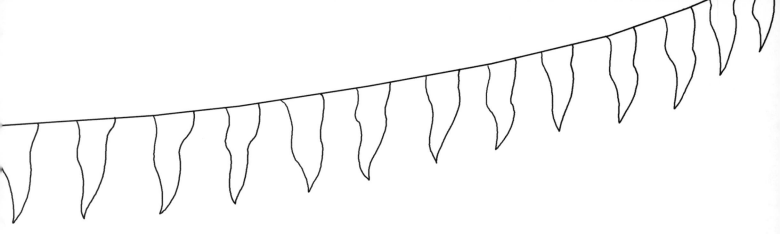

In honor of _____'s great victory, all the human kings and queens pledge allegiance to the one true supernatural leader.

Draw the victor and his new royal allies into the scene.

Following the final vampires vs werewolves battle, the allies of the losing side are rounded up and thrown into jail.

Throw the creatures who helped the losing side into this dark dungeon.

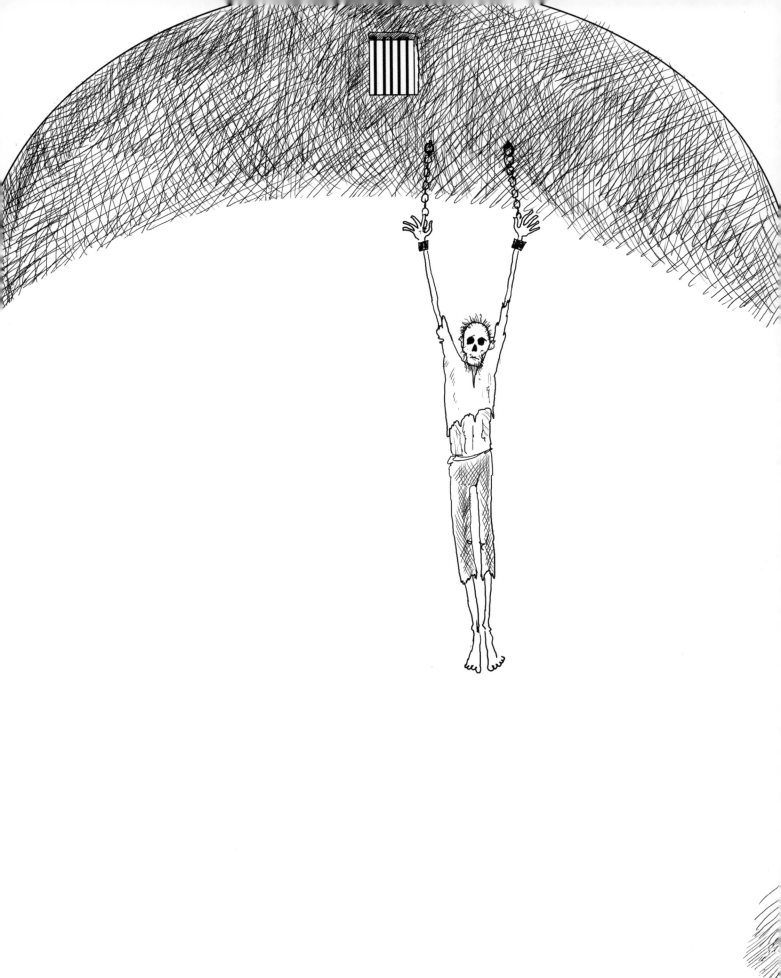

_____ is crowned king of all _____s and a special crown and scepter are made for the coronation.

Finish the designs and include a new insignia for the winning warrior.

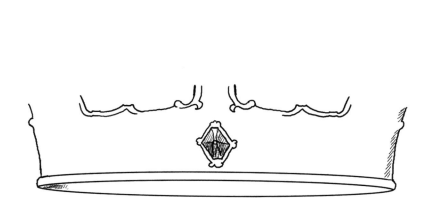

At the coronation, _____ promises that there will
be lasting peace between vampires and werewolves.

Add more happy supernatural beings
into this amphitheater scene.

The war between the vampire clans and werewolf packs is over, but what hideous creatures are plotting to become the next supreme supernatural being?

Use the stickers to decorate your doodle war pictures, then color them in.